I7TH CENTURY PAINTINGS *from the Low Countries*

17TH CENTURY PAINTINGS *from* the Low Countries

By CREIGHTON GILBERT

An exhibition of the POSES INSTITUTE OF FINE ARTS *at the* ROSE ART MUSEUM *Brandeis University Waltham, Massachusetts February 27 – March 27 1966.*

Introduction

OR a dozen years or a little longer, it has been a continuing pleasure for me to watch the growth of the collection of paintings here exhibited for the first time, with modest anonymity. It has grown greatly in size, and also in quality and selectivity. At the same time it has acquired a special slant which perhaps has not been fully expressed even by its creator.

Only a fraction of its content is presented to the public here, and the choices were not made by the owner, but by me. Hence the original viewpoint in the collecting has been overlaid by another; that being so, some suggestions about Dutch painting as it is shown to us by these examples may be added also.

This is not the place for a general sketch of painting in the Netherlands in the seventeenth century, nor is either space or competence available. An even more summary formulation of the conventional ideas about this art, cited only to be questioned, would be as follows: the most frequent approach of the artists involves two factors, first, a strong adherence to realism in the representation of materially visible things, people, the environment of town and landscape, still life from the table or kitchen, and a rejection of the imaginary, the literary, the historical, the religious, all that is not available to the eye here and now. Second, the approach involves specialization: an artist will tend to restrict himself not just to still life, but to dishes rather than vegetables, not just to landscape but to the coast rather than the forest; and he will repeat his specialty with slight variations through his career. He may have two or occasionally more specialties, but they remain two threads and do not build him into a wide-ranging artist. Within this pattern, the conventional formulation adds, there looms Rembrandt, the exception to both rules, an artist of the imaginary and the religious (although by trade a portrait painter) and one whose varied exploration of all themes is so wide as to free him from the pigeonhole of thematic dependence.

In terms of reasonable human behavior in history, how can we understand this exception? Its awkwardness is usually handled by paying tribute to Rembrandt's genius, but the exhibition suggests another answer. First, however, we should give notice to the ways in which of course it confirms the formulation. A number of the paintings exemplify the artists working on their well-known specialties, and incidentally show the high perfection of imagery thus developed. Such pictures are the famous and classic Kalf, the Van der Neer, and most extremely the Wynants, whose status within its artist's range is reported in the note on it. These allow us to ponder the implication of such repetition. Sometimes modern observers either find this astonishing, or analyze it dismissingly as commercial, exposing the artist as a manufacturer of a known successful product. Yet some of these images were maintained in the teeth of public indifference, and they should not really seem surprising when our artists, from Marin and Feininger to Hopper and Davis to Pollock and Kline to Noland and Johns, hardly do anything else but repeat, producing endless examples of what the familiarized viewer always calls "a Johns." We might also make an analogy with the jazz performer, who repeats a small repertory and who obtains response from instant recognizability of his stylistic tone. All this involves rapport with the viewer and a greater or less commercial awareness, but primarily it means that, as Henry James would have said, the artist has found his "note."

Along with these paintings, the exhibition includes a spectacular range of non-typical works. A religious image by Gabriel Metsu, an Italian peasant scene by Gerrit Berckheyde, a scene of soldier life by the youthful De Hooch, and what seems to be a unique Greek mythology by Ostade, will fascinate the expert visitor as counterpoints to the artists' known habits. Indeed it emerges that most Dutch artists experimented with exceptions to their rules. Here, exceptions like the Ostade and the Metsu are homages to Rembrandt's impact, but more broadly it is suggestive that the exceptions by many artists, when not specifically in Rembrandt's style, are worked from imagination as much as from observation. That is, they make a link between Rembrandt and the other artists, rather than allowing him to be seen as a jolting exception.

The exhibition also illustrates other more or less familiar "exceptions." The Utrecht school was a stimulus to Rembrandt, with its monumental and rather literary figure paintings, but has always been set apart as a special case that doesn't count. It is presented here in a work exceptional in it, the magnificent Knupfer, and in the Bloemaert. The latter also exemplifies another agreed-on exception, the Italianate landscape. In it, landscape view ceases to be a realistic report, and develops fanciful decorative shapes which embody emotional evocations. This art too has been recognized, and was practised by a surprisingly large number of artists. But it has again been set aside, and labeled trivial because it is artificial, which makes a circular analysis. Recently it has been more noticed, and we might add that imaginative landscape uses not only Italy, but the Norwegian fir forests of Ruysdael. Thus it is a bridge between Van Schooten's plate of meat and Metsu's Abraham. Generally, then, the exhibition has a valuable bias towards this art in which the Netherlanders spread out from observation toward imagination in many ways, including Rembrandt's. These works are statistically rare, but that has wrongly led to their being excluded from descriptions of the pattern. They should add to our comprehension and admiration.

C. G.

Catalogue

The paintings have been selected from a private collection in New York. In addition to the paintings catalogued, the exhibition comprises a group of etchings by Rembrandt and two artists connected with him, Lastman and Bol, in fine impressions from the same collection.

In the notes on the paintings, height precedes width of measurement. All the paintings are in oil unless otherwise specified.

Photographic credits: Eric Pollitzer, John Schiff, Brenwasser, New York.

I. Jan Bruegel the elder (1568-1625)

The Procession into the Ark

Oak panel, 30¼ x 51½ in. (77 x 131 cm.)

Jan Bruegel was one year old at the death of his father, the great Pieter Bruegel. They belong to one of the greatest and largest dynasties of painters, and Jan is called "velvet Bruegel" to distinguish him from various relatives and in compliment to his technical skills. The *Ark* makes a good introduction to this exhibition partly because it evokes many of the typical artistic interests of its generation in Antwerp, then the chief city of the Low Countries. Of course as the theme is expounded to us, it is revealed as an excuse to proffer an encyclopedia of animals, almost a visual list of a whole category of material reality. This indefatigable feeling for microscopic truth is a very old Flemish tradition, which Pieter Bruegel had modified in his own way. Jan modifies it again, using it as the carrier for luxurious ornamental patterns, marked by happy virtuosity in their sharp jumps for the eye, shiny and rich textures and graceful curving lines. The unlikely blend of realism and decoration, both remaining intense, is possible because Jan was in addition involved with the late phase of mannerism, a style whose love of a paradoxical or artificial distortion of reality was now being pushed so far that it came full circle, producing a tight, fixed, glare of reality as the final twist. This type of mannerism and the old Flemish realism are basic to the period; Jan's elegant ornamentation is his own, and the blend is his link to his age. Famous and successful, he and his associates often repeated their forms; the pair of lions, the tiger and the parrots seen here recur exactly in other paintings. As usual, the big workshop like a law firm today divided up the tasks, and the human figures and the landscape here are by two associates of the master, of debatable identity.

2. Floris Van Schooten (ca. 1590-ca. 1655)

Still Life with a Platter of Meat
Oak panel, 18⅛ x 33½ in. (46 x 85 cm.)
Signed with monogram and dated, *FvS fecit 1627*

The town of Haarlem, then the third or fourth largest in the nation and having its own character although only eleven miles from Amsterdam, has one of the best claims to be the place where seventeenth century Dutch art first emerged, with a distinct character, from the Flemish or general Netherlandish tradition. Around 1610 it certainly produced in Frans Hals the first immortal artist belonging to that context; in addition to Hals as a portrait specialist the Haarlem landscapist Esaias van de Velde seems more than anyone else to be the influential father of the great spread of that specialized art. The little known Floris van Schooten may have somewhat the same relation to still life, at least in respect to his surprisingly early career, and he has an interesting parallelism to Van de Velde. Considered as designers, both tend to assemble their realistic properties with a rather loose horizontal line-up that gives respectful emphasis to the independent reality of each natural thing, but yet provides an austere and plain unity. The latter is in contrast to the exuberant sprawling sensuousness of earlier Flemish accumulative painting (as in Jan Bruegel's animals) and is a pioneering move toward the studied complexity of a Ruysdael landscape or a Kalf still life. Van Schooten works with a series of detached platters, each the frame for a different kind of object. Sometimes the rhythm is a simple equal beat; here the central chunk of meat pulls the forms tighter, and its surprising juicy character also has a Haarlem-like relish, as in Hals' drinkers and Brouwer's peasants. Van Schooten was so little known around 1900 that his span of activity was only from 1627 to 1639, nor was it even understood that he was a still life painter. Awareness of his importance can be expected to increase.

3. Moses Van Uyttenbroeck (ca. 1595-1646)

Arcadian Shepherds
Oak panel, 10⅞ x 7⅞ in. (27.6 x 20 cm.)

Uyttenbroeck reminds us that there is a constant minority strain in Netherlandish painting which is dissatisfied with imagery of the nearby world of facts. Its bent toward imagination and dreams is supported by an appeal to Italy, to the classical world, and to literature. At this period it is reinforced by the originality and talent of painters like Elsheimer, of whom Uyttenbroeck has sometimes been considered a pupil. Yet it is striking that, as Stechow has commented, Uyttenbroeck is one of the very few artists who was able to absorb the poetic and superior feeling of the classic into the plain and even naive local attitudes. Here that ability is beautifully presented in the painting of the back. It is realistic and irregular to the point of ugliness. Yet it does not contradict the mood of the painting, which is dreamy and meditative, qualities developed by the sense of imprecise location, unspecified subject, stillness and solidity. The effect evoked, combining academic classic nudes with detachment from space and with a sense of physical awkwardness or inadequacy, is a permanent one, as the blue period of Picasso suggests. In its own time it is closer to Rembrandt, who sometimes uses similar patterns to produce his confrontations between human dignity and weakness. In the fertile collision between high-class artistic allusion and ordinary recording, Uyttenbroeck has a place which this work demonstrates as few others by him do. It is unusually small among the sixty-odd known paintings. It may be significant that he worked in The Hague, not a major art center but the nearest thing in Holland to a royal court.

Former collection: Rothmann, London.
Publication: U. Weisner, "Katalog der Gemaelde Van Uyttenbroecks," *Oud Holland,* 1964, no. 4, Cat. No. 40.

13

4. Bartholomeus Breenbergh (1599-ca. 1657)

Martyrdom of St. Stephen
Oak panel, 26⅜ x 37⅜ in. (67 x 95 cm.)
Signed and dated 1632

Artists of the seventeenth century went to Rome from every country, as to Paris in the early twentieth, and some remained for years or all their lives. The Netherlanders among them, though drawn to a center of art and of classical heritage, naturally sketched and painted the realistic details of their environment, as they were trained to do at home, producing the equivalent of the modern tourist's snapshot album and most of our records of how Rome looked. There is thus a whole category of the Dutch Roman landscape, fascinatingly accurate and sharp, but always a little affected by a feeling for the exotic richness of the ancient civilization, so that it is softened and given sentiment or made rhythmic with bold composition. Breenbergh stayed in Rome for seven years, returning about 1630, the year of his earliest known work. Thus this panel belongs to his first full development, and suggests his response of excitement in its high-keyed lighting and its boldly wrought rocking balances of weighted forms. The excitement and the sense of historic remoteness are further enhanced by the violent figures. In this period, small figures in a big landscape are called *staffage;* it was a time when pure landscape was becoming interesting, but wasn't fully admitted as justifiable, so the figures are the excuse for the subject. They represent the first Christian martyrdom, a suitably Roman subject. According to the text, St. Paul, not yet a disciple, was an idle witness; here he appears large and mocking, and, for added piquancy, may be a self-portrait of Breenbergh.

Former collections: probably the painting auctioned Amsterdam, November 30, 1772, no. 87, and in the J. D. Nyman sale, Amsterdam, August 16, 1797, no. 27, and the one in the Cardinal Fesch collection, Rome, (*Catalogue,* 1841, no. 289) dispersed in the sale of March 25, 1844, no. 29. (Data courtesy of H. Gerson.) General J. C. Delafield, U. S. Army.

5. Jacobus Sibrandi Mancadan (1602-1680)

Travellers among Mountains
Oak panel, 15⅛ x 15 in. (38.5 x 38 cm.)

Since Holland is a very small country, it is hard to realize the importance of the fact that its large cities and its artists were concentrated overwhelmingly (as its cities still are) in the southwestern quarter: Amsterdam, Rotterdam, Haarlem, Leiden, Delft, are all within commuting distance. This makes it possible for the northeastern areas of Groningen and Frisia, near the German border, to seem strange and remote, a quality reinforced by their sandy, marshy landscape, and at this period by their political separateness and different dialect. This is one of the reasons why Mancadan, one of the few artists of the region, has remained very obscure, being the only artist of this exhibition not listed in the great Wurzbach dictionary of Dutch painters. The other reason is that he rarely signed his works (seventeenth century Holland seems to have established the practice of most artists to sign most of their works). Only two signatures are known, one of an untypical display piece, the other (Stuve collection, Osnabruck) a work particularly close to this one. Mancadan's landscape, however, is not local, but imaginary. By coincidence, the remarkable feeling of lonely wastes also evokes for us the detached strangeness of his province, but he, perhaps with that as a starting point, invented mountains with an extraordinary, subtle, pallor of air, a tone as of light brown sugar dissolved in light. The tightly clustered family, whose journey seems so desolate and so inexplicable, only enhances the feeling. Thus the art of Mancadan is tantalizingly romantic, at the opposite extreme from conventional descriptions of the Dutch.

Former collection: Douglas, Dublin (sale Sotheby, London, 1957).

18

6. Nicolaus Knupfer (ca. 1603-1660)

Solon before Croesus
Oak panel, 23¼ x 34½ in. (59 x 87.5 cm.)
Signed lower left

Born in Leipzig, Knupfer came to Holland in his twenties as a refugee from the Thirty Years War. He settled in Utrecht, the most Catholic town in Holland, which seems also to have encouraged the emergence of un-Dutch artists, interested less in the here and now than in the literary, classical, and religious, and in painting compositions of large dramatic figures in the Italian or Flemish way. Knupfer seems to have painted at least five compositions of this story, in which the Athenian lawgiver Solon, a prisoner of the very wealthy king Croesus, told him: "Call no man happy until he is dead." (This moral proverb was still culturally alive in the nineteenth century world of the classically educated American newspaper reader, who used the phrase "rich as Croesus" and used "Solons" as a headline synonym for "Senators.") Knupfer's repetitions of the theme, in works of differing scale, are only an element of his broad interest in scenes in which a lower-status petitioner or defendent appears before a judge or king. These include David playing to Saul, the Judgment of Solomon, Zorobabel before Darius, the Feast of Herod, Christ before Pilate, Paul before Festus, and the Clemency of Scipio. All allow a dramatic balance of psychological energies to work through a Baroque imbalance of up and down. The varnish-brown overall tone which Knupfer uses with such shining virtuosity, and the spotlighting, are generally Rembrandtesque, and the emergence from them of twisted stringbean people is very like the little known Leonard Bramer. But the odd and bold emphasis, along with the varnish, on strawberry pink, underlines Knupfer's most incongruous element of success, his wittiness, which he certainly imparted to his great pupil Jan Steen. Yet these links in no way diminish his extremely personal note.

Publications: E. Plietsch, *Hollaendische und Vlaemische Maler des XVII Jahrhunderts*, Leipzig, 1960, pp. 33-34, Plate 32; J. I. Kouznetzow, "Nikolaus Knupfer, biographie, themes et sources de la creation artistique, catalogue des oeuvres," (in Russian, with French summary) in *Trudy Gosudarstvennogo Ermitazha, Zapadnoevropeiskoe Iskusstvo*, VIII, Moscow, 1965, p. 221, cat. no. 113.

7. Aert Van der Neer (1603-1677)

River Landscape by Moonlight
Oak panel, 12 x 18½ in. (30.5 x 47 cm.)
Signed with monogram, lower left

Van der Neer is a typical citizen of his native Amsterdam, which encouraged in its artists the development of personal trademarks and self-confident presentations, with more variety and urbane suavity than any other Dutch city. Yet he appears to have begun as an amateur, painting his first known works when over thirty; this accounts for the technical roughness of his surfaces, which, pushed to expressive extremes, are often in poor preservation. His unmistakable trademark is the night landscape, of which some hundreds can be found, almost black and white as the moonlight articulates it. They are often most attractive in small scale, because the theme also calls for an almost smudged vagueness of optical tone, unlike usual works of art in black and white which for the most part are based on line drawing. The importance of this soft tone to Van der Neer is confirmed by his second most common choice, the snow landscape, equally a colorless continuum. The night scenes typically center on a river, still further avoiding sharpness. This softly shadowed river scene is certainly a major ancestor of the nineteenth century sentimental landscapes of Corot, and its romantic suggestiveness once again contradicts the alleged matter-of-factness of Dutch painting. Yet in Van der Neer, unlike Corot, it is important that the shadowy black rests upon a tightly emphasized armature of a horizontal linear base (the river bank) interwoven with small insistent verticals (masts, chimneys, tree-trunks, men). These detail elements are absent only when the night or snow is also absent. The use of an important geometric base for the composition is typical of the mid-century developed phase of Dutch specialty painting, whether landscape, still life or other, in contrast with the more open, object-oriented realism of an older generation of artists less centered on Amsterdam.

Former collection: Paul Schwabach, Berlin.

8. Adriaen Bloemaert (after 1609-1666)

Landscape with a Ford
Canvas, 21⅝ x 16⅞ in. (55 x 43 cm.)
Signed lower left

The Bloemaert family of Utrecht produced many artists, as often happened in the seventeenth century Netherlands. One of them, Abraham, is much the best known, so that his son Adriaen's personality has been obscured more than a neutral situation would have done it; this has also happened to Jan Bruegel and others. Adriaen shares with his family only the Utrecht taste for the Italianate and the general classical and literary implications of that culture. He went to Italy, and afterwards stayed some time in Salzburg. These southern years, when he was actively working, may account for a style in which the imagery of landscape is not only non-Dutch, but not naturalistic at all, having instead the decorative quality usually associated with very large ornamental murals in Baroque villas. It is this pattern, connected with such residents of Rome as the Frenchman Dughet rather than with any Dutchman (it is perhaps nearest to Jan Both), that produces the tendency to a rather thin-stretched sweep of luminous, undetailed areas. The upright format with the huge translucent clouds, the impossibly scaled trees in silhouette, the castle on a hill in the middle distance, the nicely dressed travellers fording the quiet broad stream, are all elements which recur in Adriaen in slightly rearranged combinations, as frequently as his emphatic signature. Yet its compression here to a small scale suddenly endows it with seriousness, as if it were here that the artist stopped to look at it closely.

9. Adrien Van Ostade (1610-1684)

Mercury and Argus
Oak panel, 11¾ x 12 in. (30 x 30.5 cm.)
Signed with initials

This astonishing little picture is the only one by the artist of a subject from mythology, among hundreds of works, and simultaneously is probably unique technically in its thick, sketchy roughness. Yet it has been readily accepted as his work, probably for two reasons. The first is that, among themes from myth, this is really not different from the most ordinary subject of the artist, typical of Haarlem, the cheerful and somewhat rowdy life of peasants. Mercury is a young workingman having fun, Argus an old codger having a nap. The myth is a whimsical variant on the theme, a heightening of the usual. Velazquez' *Bacchus and the Peasants*, perhaps about ten years earlier, is a classic example of the same mood. The single work in an unusual category is not itself unusual; of over a hundred known works by Adrien's brother Isaac Van Ostade, there is just one portrait. Combining both comments, one of Adrien's rare religious paintings, the *Adoration of the Shepherds*, is really another rearrangement of the same elements: shepherds, dog, cow. The second cause of the easy absorption of the painting into the artist's known activity is its close link to a group of his very tiny etchings, just as this is an exceptionally small painting. Several show two confronted figures, including a seated man listening to a piper (Bartsch etching catalogue no. 38), a five-inch print of about 1642, a still smaller smoker and drinker (B. 13), or two gossips (B. 40). Tiniest of all, a profile head is as rough in style as this painting and as another odd one with no human actors, the *Pigpen* in the Louvre. These paintings, quick and eccentric, may well have been private sketches, not to be shown. Not like Ostade's first blue and pink works, they belong with a second group of early works much influenced by Rembrandt's lighting and texture.

Publications: Catalogue of Paintings by Old Masters, Alfred Brod, London, 1956, no. 24;
Burlington Magazine, 1956, p. 420.

10. Jan Mienze Molenaer (ca. 1610-1668)

Tavern with a Woman Fiddler
Oak panel, 17¾ x 24⅜ in. (45 x 62 cm.)
Signed, on the table leg

A Haarlemer for most of his life, Molenaer belongs to the tradition of celebrating cheerful or forceful lower class social groups, firmly installed there by Haarlem's two greatest artists, Frans Hals and Adriaen Brouwer, whose original ancestor was Pieter Bruegel in Flanders. Molenaer's wife was Judith Leyster, the most notable woman painter of seventeenth century Holland and a faithful pupil of Hals. But for some years in middle life they lived in Amsterdam (where another contact was their lodger Jan Lievens, Rembrandt's earliest close associate) and that stay may symbolize, at least, the change in Molenaer's later work. The peasants are cleaned up, and so is the painting, more polished and more suavely colorful. In some two hundred later paintings, with no further noticeable change, he rearranges the few elements of the scene which we see here. Even the curved ceiling and the barrel are frequently shown, as well as the woman musician (though she may play various instruments). This is in contrast to the harder, plainer works of his youth, with fewer large figures and crude violence of theme, such as tooth pulling. The later style shares the taste of many Amsterdam painters at mid-century for a thoroughly woven design of equalized energy overall; it appears regardless of theme, as we see it in the landscapes of Van der Neer and the still life of Kalf, and tends to accompany elegance of texture each time. In peasant scenes it also transforms the art of the purely Haarlem painter Ostade.

11. Jacob De Wet the elder (ca. 1610-ca. 1671)

Salome Receiving the Head of John the Baptist
Oak panel, 14⅛ x 20⅞ in. (36 x 53 cm.)
Signed at bottom center

Though he lived in Haarlem, De Wet's career was determined by the years which he seems to have spent as a Rembrandt pupil in Amsterdam, about 1630-32. He absorbed Rembrandt at his most operatically exciting, with the violence of events underscored by focused spotlights and yawning shadows. Like many of the pupils who were faithful to the master's dramatic and luminary ideas, he could not follow him in surface technique, and completely opposes the later Rembrandt's personal shorthand and its intimate broken informality with his polished glitter and sheen. It is consistent with this that Salome is a fine lady in a feathered hat, which tradition does not demand. This is rather like Gerard Dou, the Rembrandt pupil admired perhaps more than any other in his own time. But De Wet is closer to Rembrandt than Dou is in the tautness of his theatrical concentration, comparable in this respect and in the thin tall figure types to Knupfer and perhaps to a trace of late mannerist tradition of elongated people. Indeed De Wet might be called a "mannerist Dou", if that is conceivable. He likes a special sort of drama, involving a sudden, startling or unusual confrontation between two people or groups, as in Christ with the Adulteress, Christ blessing the Children, Elijah with Ahab, and his favorite theme the Resurrection of Lazarus. The specific content of the subject seems to have interested him less than the dramatic tone and luminary design, for one of his few publicly visible works, "Meleager Presenting the slain Calydonian Boar to Atalanta" (Glasgow Museum) is almost interchangeable with this Salome, the same lady in the hat in the same spotlight with the same kneeling man. Thus De Wet has a well organized special way of working, which can become better known.

12. Bartholomeus Van der Helst (1613-1670)

Portrait of a Boy with a Silver Chalice
Canvas, 25 x 20 in. (63.5 x 51 cm.)
Signed and dated 1657

Born in Haarlem, Van der Helst settled in Amsterdam at twenty-three and is a typical Amsterdam artist in his easy sophistication. He was a portrait painter to the rich and to leaders of society, whom he satisfied by recording their conspicuously fine clothing in a skillful and dashing way, and by giving the portrait an un-Dutch mobility, with figures swinging to the side without loss of substantiality, a pattern almost Baroque in the sense of Rubens' aristocratic portraits. But the people are not flattered or idealized; they would not have expected that in this realistic bourgeois world. Indeed Van der Helst's most famous work is of a Burgermaster Bicker, with cheeks so fat that he looks foolish, and this boy is so comically a small edition of the same that he may be his son. Another high-toned habit of Van der Helst's portraits, and another component of their liveliness, are the identifying objects that the people hold. An admiral holds his staff, a preacher a book, a lady has an immense cello, the Princess of Orange (daughter of Charles I and mother of William III of England) has naturally an orange, the artist Paul Potter his easel. This chalice, as Baroque in its heavy curves and as shining as the rest of the painting, is probably by the great silversmith Jan Lutma, whose portrait Rembrandt etched in 1656. Since it must be intended to identify the boy, it may have been the christening gift.

It is conventionally said that when Rembrandt painted the Night Watch he lost his popularity as a portraitist to more fashionable artists, whom Van der Helst would represent. Seymour Slive recently showed that the neglect of Rembrandt was a myth of the romantic period, like *La Bohème*. Rembrandt became poor ten years later in a general depression. Van der Helst was indeed still popular, yet he too had little money; evidently either the commissions were few (just a hundred paintings from thirty-five years of work survive) or the fees were low. Thus as a villain or the foil in Rembrandt's career Van der Helst is not very effective.

Former collection: T. M. Kennion.

31

13. Bonaventura Peeters (1614-1652)

Sailboats at Hoboken, Flanders
Canvas, 12½ x 19¾ in. (31.7 x 50.2 cm.)
Signed with monogram on the pole

The great art of Flanders in the seventeenth century, supported by great predecessors in earlier periods, was abruptly halted when, around 1640, three of its four most distinguished artists died (Rubens, Van Dyck, Brouwer) and the fourth lapsed into permanent decline (Jordaens). The upstart habits of work in the Dutch centers acquired a monopoly of creative energy. The Antwerp artist Peeters illustrates this magnetism in a quite curious way. He was a seascape specialist, painting small panels of little variety in composition, interesting to the buyer because of the vividly evoked reality of a familiar truth, modest in mood as well as in scale. This is so unlike Antwerp artists that even a modern Belgian art historian refers to Peeters as humbly holding on to a little appreciated kind of work. Rubens, Van Dyck, and Jordaens, like most artists of the world, have their unity in their style of drawing and painting, and their subjects are almost universal. Brouwer was a specialist, but he worked some of the time in Holland, and Peeters is obviously simply adopting a Dutch procedure, almost a Dutch social psychology. Not only is realistic thumbnail specialty painting at this period mainly Dutch, but Peeters, who in Antwerp terms gives the impression of having invented the realistic seascape, is actually greatly in the debt of Dutch seascape painters, especially Porcellis. On the other hand, the boldness of the movements of masses, the force of the right-leaning diagonals with only weak counter-diagonals, the circular areas of light with unfinished shifting edges, are more Baroque than any Dutch painter would want to emphasize, almost Rubensian; Peeters retains his local background in the area of pure painting style.

Publication: Le Siècle de Rubens, Brussels, 1965, No. 163.

14. Emanuel De Witte (1617-1692)

Interior of a Catholic Church
Oak panel, 16⅛ x 12¾ in. (41 x 32.3 cm.)
Signed lower left on bench

A specialized Dutch painter did not simply stay with landscape or still life, he stayed with sand dunes or apples, and De Witte is the trademarked painter of church interiors. The recent catalogue of his works shows 198 of them, out of 255 works. Many are particular identifiable ones, in the Dutch realistic recording manner, so the amount of variation needed to produce this Catholic church, which De Witte never saw and produced out of his head, is far more than one would think at first. Doubtless it was assisted by engravings of Italian buildings, especially St. Peter's (the roundels in the spandrels just under the dome suggest it) but modified, notably in the Gothic apse. There are some seven paintings of this or a very similar late Renaissance Catholic church, and one in the Zurich museum is most similar. It is dated 1685 and this is probably still later, a smaller variant. Unlike most repetitive artists, De Witte notably grew in vitality more and more into his old age, and this late work typically shows a deft lightness and sketchiness of touch which is hardly to be anticipated in such a geometric design. It is the happiness of familiar mastery. It is easy to think of De Witte as a designer, making slight variations on these light and dark blocks, and thus as a prophet of Mondrian. Such a link is meaningful only if we think of De Witte as one of a group of specialized artists of his generation, whose works are all refined designs, like Mondrian, whether they are buildings or vegetables. Although this imaginary church suggests the artist as a free inventor of forms, it was probably painted on order; he also painted some Gothic Catholic churches, and both types are marked by the same two monks.

Former collections: Viscount Weymouth (sale London 1944); A. Welker, London, 1951; Mrs. Angela van Praag (sale London, 1954); Sidney van den Berberg, 1956.
Publication: I. Manke, *Emanuel de Witte*, Amsterdam, 1963, cat. 150.

15. JanVictors (1620-1676)

The Expulsion of Hagar
Canvas, 55½ x 70⅞ in. (141 x 180 cm.)
Signed and dated 1650

Victors is a relatively little known pupil of Rembrandt, who was with him in Amsterdam about 1640. It is always remarked that his early work, closer to his master, is his best, and this painting at age thirty is certainly among his most distinguished. From Rembrandt he has learned to come up very close to the human being, to make it heroically monumental, and to explore its keenest feelings and stresses at times of pressure. The necessary interlocking of human grandeur and human weakness is Rembrandt's essential legacy, most difficult to imitate because it is very near the edge of empty academicism on one side or swollen sentimentality on the other. All the pupils, not being Rembrandt, had to become involved in one of these difficulties, and Victors settled for an element of the academic. His rejection of softness has a positive, tough-minded aspect in the absolute firmness of his line drawing and the restrained, exquisitely right harmonies of brown and purple. In this firm way he saves his potentially very sentimental subject, the mother and boy driven from home by the edict of the chief wife. Victors in fact likes themes involving pathos of family or childhood situations, which are Rembrandtesque anyway; he represented the Clothing of the Poor, Jacob blessing Joseph, the Massacre of the Innocents, Esther before Ahasuerus. In moving beyond Rembrandt to a more academic drawing style, Victors again chose the best, taking as his model the greatest achievement of academic soundness of drawing, the Bologna school. This work in particular is so like Guercino in many details of texture and motifs that it is a puzzle how they were available to him.

Former collection: Oskar Bondi, Vienna.
Publication: R. Hamann, "Hagars Abschied bei Rembrandt und im Rembrandtkreis," *Marburger Jahrbuch,* 8-9, 1936, p. 501ff., fig. 43.

38

16. Carel Dujardin (ca. 1622-1678)

Peasants by a Waterhole
Canvas, 16⅛ x 15 in. (41 x 38 cm.)
Signed and dated 1667

The pull of Italy on Dujardin is symbolized by the fact that he not only made the commonplace young man's trip there, but returned with friends in mature life, lingering behind them until he died in Venice. Imagery of longing for Italy is a fact of the art of northern Europe in general, of Germany (Goethe's *Kennst du das Land wo die Zitroenen bluehn*) of England (from Milton's Vallombrosa to D. H. Lawrence's Etruscan places). In seventeenth century Holland it was strong enough in painters and patrons to produce a whole specialist school whose realistic landscape and peasant genre was not local, but Roman. Moved by exotic yearnings, it also loses some elements of its realism, and perhaps for the first time establishes the figure of the picturesque peasant, the standardized figure who survives so familiarly in *Cavalleria rusticana*. Marked by too cheerful costumes and by suggestive ruined buildings, this art is perhaps most uniformly evocative through its luminous tone, designed to recall the southern sun, and produced through translucency of paint application. In this case Dujardin shows his consciousness of it by focusing his composition of masses, thicker as they recede, on the handsome brass vessel on the girl's head. Dujardin's personal composition very often involves, as here, a close attachment of figures to earth, lying on it or drinking from a stream. He is usually cited as developing under the influence of the older Italianate landscapist Berchem, but this view contains some limited Netherlandish views. This painting has its closest source in Pieter Van Laer, who moved to Italy permanently and was called Bamboccio, and in his pupil Cerquozzi, who saw his own Italy through Dutch eyes and often painted such small rectangular notes of conversation before a looming wall.

Former collection: Charles Butler, London (sale 1876).

17. Willem Kalf (1622-1693)

Still Life with Goblets and Lemon
Canvas, 27⅛ x 22⅞ in. (69 x 58 cm.)

If this gorgeous assemblage gives the impression of a particularly fine and classic example of Kalf, there is a reason: it was itself responsible, when exhibited at the New York World's Fair in 1940, for making him widely known to American museum goers, starting a process which now normally tags him as the greatest Dutch still life painter. But even apart from that it is a full-throttled statement of Kalf at his most brilliant, from the spiral lemon peel, his most familiar trick, to the series of glasses (from the left: a *roemer*, a *façon-de-Venise* goblet, and a flute-glass). Kalf here is a typical Amsterdam painter in the urbane suavity with which he embraces these objects; like his contemporary Van der Helst the portraitist, he makes realism serve the Baroque and the rich, by restricting reality to a narrow range. Considered as abstract designs, these mature works after 1650 show the same strongly organized horizontal-vertical structuring that is visible in the contemporary Amsterdamers Van der Neer and De Witte. Here, specifically, transparent cylindrical verticals lift up lightly from a sprawling base of opaque oval horizontals; the conch shell is intermediate in shape, in surface, and in location. So highly studied an arrangement pays its respects to the beauty of the objects which it adjusts. Since Kalf is generally supposed to have been influenced in his youth by Rembrandt's lighting effects, one might suspect, again abstractly, that this type of composition reflects Rembrandt's development in the 1640's of a "subdued Baroque" compositional design, mobile, but increasingly centralized, and dominated by repeated vertical cylinders. The Night Watch and the Hundred Guilder Print are the classic examples.

Former collections: Kaiser Wilhelm II, Doorn, Holland; Eugene Garbaty, New York.
Publications: Masterpieces of Art, New York, 1940, no. 104; T. Buechner, *Glass Vessels in Dutch Paintings of the 17th Century,* Corning, N. Y., 1952, p. 25.

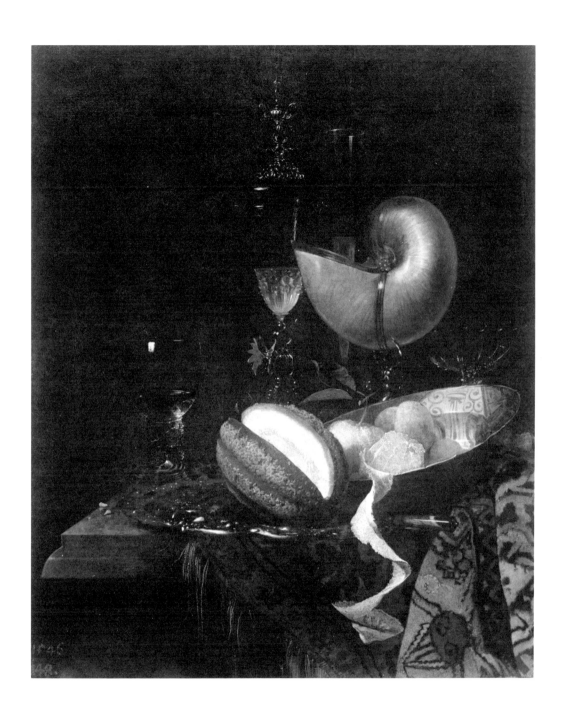

41

18. Adam Pynacker (1622-1673)

Mountain Landscape
Oak panel, 15⅛ x 13 in. (38.5 x 33 cm.)

Pynacker is not much known or studied as an individual, aside from the awareness of small personal tricks that distinguish him within his group. Chiefly he is regarded as a typical member of that large group, the Italianate landscape painters, to which in different ways Adriaen Bloemaert and Carel Dujardin also belong. Pynacker is close to Jan Both, and in principle recalls Adriaen Bloemaert, in that his most familiar works are large decorative wall paintings, allowing the broth-colored open sky, with large dusty mountain and tall splindly tree, to grow an expressive scale of openness, mass, or extension. Those works are also conspicuously sharp-focused, so much so that this one with its slightly pastier tone is not at once to be spotted as his. It shares this textural variation, however, with a smaller quantity of works in this more modest scale, such as those in the Louvre and the Liechtenstein collection. It is especially similar to one in the Boymans collection, about three inches higher and wider than this, with which it also shares the same cattle and mountain. What is more basic to Pynacker's view is the zig-zag design, readable both in two and in three dimensions, which determines the portioning and the lighting of his forms.

Former collections: Hans Wendland, Paris; Hans Fritz Fankhauser, Basel.

19. Pieter De Hooch (1629-ca. 1684)

Soldiers Quartered in a Barn
Oak panel, 26 x 24¾ in. (66 x 63 cm.)
Signed on the three-legged stool

This painting, with its complex forms and final vitality, must be one of the most rewarding to the exhibition visitor, as it is the most significant revelation to the specialist. The great Pieter De Hooch is well known as second only to Vermeer among the Dutch specialty painters concerned with domestic scenes, the family life in rooms that has been called "polite genre" in distinction from the rowdy tavern genre. His cool, architectonic figures in warm light, the adjustment of the box of space to the poised human being, have a meaningfulness equally in design and in social commentary that is more reinforced by their interplay than most observers of either are consciously aware. Less known, but a revealing clue to their qualities, is the very early work of De Hooch, like this painting. It differs from the usual ones in subject, being concerned with soldier life, a less polite interest, and connected to older painters like Pieter Codde and Jacob Duck. This first phase is difficult to see satisfactorily; only two signed examples have been known until now, and many of the other attributions are problems. This is especially close to one of the two (Berlin, Vogel collection) with the same standing woman, while a very different but fine one is the unsigned work in the North Carolina Museum, a soldier waking up in a pile of straw and kicking out his legs. In general it has been noted that "the quietest ones are the best" and this work indeed fascinates by the cool, almost static precision with which it presses down on its exuberant actors. Traditionally casual in its preconditions, it develops evidently through mere force of personality in the artist the gleaming exactitude of which he is a master.

44

45

20. Gabriel Metsu (1629-1667)

The Sacrifice of Isaac
Canvas, 24 x 18½ in. (61 x 47 cm.)

A century ago Metsu was near the head of the list of admired Dutch artists, but today is out of favor, and thus one of the best known artists on whom there is no book. We may find him sentimental, or more neutrally may think of him as expressing an intermediate feeling between De Hooch and Rembrandt: domestic family life or polite genre, along with pathos and the personal exposure of intimate emotions. In his native town of Leiden the great earlier artist had been Rembrandt, but a Rembrandt pupil, Gerard Dou, was now the chief local painter, and did indeed dilute Rembrandt into polite genre, old philosophers with nicely brushed robes. Metsu has a more substantial mix: a mother with her sick child does not dilute either type of theme, but probes both. That subject at once connects with this painting, Abraham expecting the death of his son. Hence as with other artists the rare non-Dutch theme, taken from the Old Testament, turns out actually to be hardly different from the usual realistic ones of the artist. Indeed Metsu's few religious paintings usually concern family distress: the expulsion of Hagar, Christ and the adulterous woman, Christ healing the sickness of Peter's mother-in-law or Jairus' daughter, the widow's mite. The list is like Victors, but even more domestic. Here the composition too is like many of Metsu's in general layout, showing a standing figure dominating a seated one lighter in tone: a drowsy landlady poked at by customers, a sick woman, and closest perhaps an elderly maid combing a girl's hair, startlingly distant in theme. These analogies may make clear why this undocumented painting has been accepted as Metsu's work so readily. Yet despite the factors of assimilation, the religious paintings all seem to be early; of Metsu's dated works, the second and third in sequence (both in 1653) have religious themes, and no others.

Former collection: F. Rothmann, London.
Publication: Rembrandt's Influence in the 17th Century, Matthiesen Gallery, London, 1953, no. 53.

21. Jan Wynants (ca. 1630-1684)

Landscape with a Hunter
Panel, 10 x 12¼ in. (25.5 x 31 cm.)
Signed center right

If ever a painter ought by rights to merit the title of a hack, it would at first seem to be Wynants. The 726 catalogued works of his career (which certainly include duplications) are limited almost exclusively not just to landscape, but, as the cataloguer summarizes, to a "wavy landscape, sandy, with a path and trees, on one side a clump of trees and on the other side a panorama." Even more specializing, he never painted the figures, these being provided by three collaborators, in this painting perhaps Adriaen van de Velde or Jan Lingelbach. This extreme narrowness prevents what would with another painter be the plausible guess that this is catalogue no. 152, twice recorded in the 18th century as "dune landscape with hunter, his weapon on his shoulder and a dog with him, in the foreground, speaking to a seated woman. In the middleground two anglers by a small body of water. View to the distance in full sunlight; may be identical with 153 and 205." But the measurements differ by two centimeters, and the painting was on canvas; no. 153 had a background mountain, and in no. 205 the woman was begging. Yet despite all this, the landscape is fresh and vivid, atmospherically warm and immediate. It is partly that, as has been noted, his small wood panels have more charm than the large canvases. But it is also that the pattern being repeated is daring and suggests the opposite of repeated convention by its looseness. The dune areas break out like blotches, trees wriggle, and a fence by Wynants has its horizontals at a different level in every unit. Spottiness, undulation and twining lines make the mood, a very sophisticated way of holding the composition together with the lightest threads. In other specialty painters of this late generation, a similar approach can be seen in some of the greatest, especially in the late work of Ruysdael and Steen.

22. Cornelis De Heem (1631-1695)

Fruit and Oysters
Canvas, 14⅛ x 21½ in. (36 x 54.5 cm.)
Signed left on the table

Cornelis De Heem, born in Holland, lived his working life in Flanders. He was the son of a more famous still life painter who was born in Flanders but worked in Holland. In this case the son did continue the tradition of the father's art as in a workshop, (unlike such artists as the younger Bruegel and the younger Bloemaert) and both show a mix of Dutch and Flemish qualities in their vocabulary, somewhat as Peeters does. As a specialty picture, concentrating hard on the reporting of the real thing nearby, such a work seems very Dutch, like a Dutch portrait or tree. But it is rather modified toward Flemish flavor in the sense of being Baroque, which in this case means that its impact is of an active and vivid mass. Movement of mass is one definition of Baroque, and the lineage of Rubens' Antwerp is detectable here, though only as a flavor.

Those qualities must be read across another set of links to other artists and trends of expression through time. The three still life oils in the exhibition are by three artists of different age groups, Schooten (born ca. 1590), Kalf (born 1622) and De Heem (born 1631). Their differences do happen to represent the evolution of still life design quite well, a first generation which is very truthful and particular, with only a primitive interest in organization; a second classic generation which builds on realism a most elegant network of harmonious composition, and a third which is marked by design to the point of dryness, as here. In some sense this is a story of Dutch painting in general, as we may (with extreme oversimplification) see it in the greatest artists of the three generations, Hals, Rembrandt, and Vermeer. (This omits most importantly an alternate third stage, to a very loose-knit pattern, as in Wynants and the great Ruysdael.) The analogy to Vermeer will suggest that to call De Heem dry is not to condemn him.

51

23. Nicolas Maes (1632-1693)

Portrait of a Scholar
Canvas, 35 x 28 in. (89 x 71 cm.)
Signed and dated 1666 on a book

Maes was, among the pupils formed in Rembrandt's studio, perhaps the most successful of all. His early work is monumental genre, scenes of domestic life which work out a corner of Rembrandt's legacy by presenting the human figure in life-size impact but in a humble capacity, yet otherwise move from it to the more ordinary Dutch concern of everyday life. Later Maes turned entirely to portraits, a move which will surprise us less when we recall that Rembrandt was among other things a leader of portrait painters, supremely polished and vigorous, as fashionable as he was realistic. Maes modifies the Rembrandt portrait style of the 1640's less than he had the compositions. His portraits are less complex and difficult in design and lighting and characterization, easier to accept, closer to a norm and a type and more centrally posed, reductions which must apply to any artist who induces a comparison with Rembrandt. But he has made us admire, nowhere more than in this splendid presentation, qualities which exist in Rembrandt but often pass unnoticed in him: solidity of form, related to expressive yielding textures, active balances of small lights against large darks, symmetrical power ornamented by irregular accidentals, which add up to synthesis of volume and vibration that is truly Rembrandtesque. Later in his life Maes' portraits grow very dry in line and texture, and fashionably French in ornamentation, but no implication of that shows here beyond the self-confident manners of the figure. It may have been painted in Antwerp, where Maes went some time between July 1665 and April 1667. Of four other portraits dated 1666, two have the same measurements as this (and one is of unknown size).

Former collections: Hans Wendland, Paris; Hans Fritz Fankhauser, Basel.
Publication: Valentiner Memorial Exhibition Catalogue, Raleigh, 1959, no. 84.

24. Cornelis Pieterszoon De Mooy

(ca. 1634-1693)

Ships and Sailboats

Grisaille wash on oak gessoed panel, 14½ x 19¼ in. (37 x 49 cm.)

Signed on the barrel

A noticeable school of ship painters could be easily predicted in seventeenth century Holland, simply on the basis of two known facts: that painters there regularly specialized in one or another object of the material environment, and that the Dutch fleet was a great one and a basic source of the national wealth. And yet it did not occur, ship painters are scarce and of minor importance. A quick inspection of the exceptions may suggest why; thus, the great sea painters like Van Goyen and Ruysdael tend to minimize ships, or, the one best known dynasty of ship painters, the Van de Velde family, is exceptional on a second count in that it emigrated permanently to England, a unique step (in contrast with the Italianate landscape painters, who stayed in Italy or kept at home in equal quantities), or, that this obscure painter Cornelis De Mooy belonged to Rotterdam, the one major town of seventeenth century Holland least rich in artists, and of course the one most specialized in shipping, as it is today. There is certainly a sense that the visual image of the ship is downgraded, that its artists unlike other specialists have lower status, like the horse painters of eighteenth century England or Currier and Ives artists. Possibly the ship as heavy industry is not a sight so agreeable in the Dutch burgher's living room as themes of recreation; in genre, the tavern is usual and the shop unusual. It may be (though not necessarily) that Mooy's extreme obscurity is part of this pattern: an encyclopedia writer of 1906 knew only six works, assembled from older catalogues of signed works (and doubted two of them, because he dated his death seventeen years too early). Another, in 1930, added just one. Yet the very distinctive style should have revealed others, closer to the three hundred known by Van de Velde. The exact diagramming of the rigging, a pleasure to hobbyists of all centuries, links Mooy with the "tight" style of other artists his age.

25. Jan Van der Heyden (1637-1712)

Houses among Trees
Oak panel, 9¼ x 10 in. (23.5 x 25.5 cm.)
Signed with monogram on the signpost

Van der Heyden is the master of the brick wall, or, as here, the brick-paved road.
In this detail of reality his effect is his own and unforgettable, so that he is its unique
master, perhaps now accompanied by Ben Shahn! It is based on straight lines in tiny
units, thus at once aligning Van der Heyden among the formalistic, "tight" artists of
his age group, of all specialties and degrees of fame, from Vermeer to Cornelis
de Heem and Mooy. But it is picked out with dots of light, so that the sense of a dry
diagram is removed and the sense of vibrating light replaces it, effecting the double
feeling of satisfaction in solid construction and breathing life. In these late seventeenth century years, when Dutch art seemed to be coming to a dead end, he is one
of the sensitive talents, even through the pervasive factor of the cut-and-dried. He is
also the leader of a group of painters of street views in towns, a specialty which
suddenly became very active in these late years (like ship-painting, with which it
shares its blueprint look), and in this way becomes one of those whose art did
stimulate later artists after all. The great eighteenth century masters of the Venetian
veduta, from Canaletto on, certainly owe much to this little group, with the
traveller to Italy Van Wittel as the most obvious intermediary. Van der Heyden
settled his style of street views in the 1660's, after travels to towns in Flanders and
Germany which he recorded (he and Canaletto both belong to the visual tradition of
the tourist post card). Later as here he enlarged the landscape elements, but retained
the points of light. Still later he turned from painting to inventions, which happily
included a street light and a fire hose.

Former collection: Major Grant-Thorold, Crawford Hall, Kettering (Northants) England.

26. Gerrit Berckheyde (1638-1698)

Peasant Family at a Ford
Oak panel, 18⅞ x 26¾ in. (48 x 68 cm.)
Signed right center

The oddness of this painting emerges only if one knows the painter. It is clearly identifiable to the eye as a quite usual Italianate landscape, with picturesque peasants, pervasive warm light, and the relatively large scale which this theme often uses (in contrast to the small examples in this exhibition by Adriaen Bloemaert and Dujardin, but somewhat like the Breenbergh). Berckheyde, however, was principally a painter of street views, like Van der Heyden, and indeed is the second leader of the group that made that art grow significant in this very late phase of Dutch painting. He varies them with seaports and church interiors, but the variation seems slight. Paintings of this kind do not seem to be on record. However, it is not necessary to find this a puzzle, since the Italian peasants and their landscape do appear normally in the artist's particularly fine drawings. Like the works by Ostade and Metsu in the exhibition, this then is a rare exception to the artist's specialty. But unlike the others, Berckheyde did not paint a rare kind of theme or image; he simply worked in the normal special imagery of other artists.

Two facts may be clues to explain this. One is the acceptable report that he always painted his own figures. Many architectural painters naturally did not, so that his interest was more than average. The other is that he always lived in Haarlem, a fact seemingly important to him only for the specific streets he records. The Haarlem feeling for peasant life, in Hals and Ostade, was now almost extinct along with any special Haarlem local style, but these peasants may be traceable to it as an indirect reflection.